Finding the Inspired Life

Finding the Inspired Life

Peter's Kingdom-driven Journey

Kathy King

Finding the Inspired Life
Peter's Kingdom-driven Journey
© 2016 by Kathy King

ISBN – 978-0692626160

Published by

His Kingdom Publishing
San Jose, California

Dedication

This book wouldn't have been made possible had it not been for the 'Greatest Inspirer' to ever walk the earth, Our Lord and Savior, Jesus Christ. Thank You Jesus for giving us Your word, the Bible, as Your perfect blueprint for our lives. Thank You for Your grace and mercy towards us as we aim to become more like You every day. It is our prayer that this book ministers to your children, young and old, and that it will let them see that it's never too early, or too late, to begin to live the inspired life. We love you Lord.

There's only one person who knows me almost as well as Jesus and that's my incredible man of God and husband, Jeff King. God gave me such a cherished gift when He gave me Jeff as my husband almost twenty seven years ago. Thank you, Jeff for believing in me and for listening to me as I read this book to you over and over. You made this work a labor of love with your support and care. Jeff, I love you very much.

Table of Contents

Acknowledgements

I would like to take this time to thank my dear friend, Karen Greenwell, who encouraged me over twelve years ago in her wonderful writer's group, to write on paper what the Lord was depositing into my heart. I took her advice and now give Jesus full credit for everything that He downloaded into my soul for this book. I also need to express my appreciation to Karen and her husband, Dan Greenwell for proof reading and editing my book with such professional care and respect. Thank you, Karen and Dan. You're the best.

My inspiration for the book came from my awesome Pastors, Dr. David Cannistraci and Pastor Chris Cobb who wrote the book, *The Inspired Life: God's Dream for Your Future.* They gave me permission to read their manuscript and to take away key topics from their book to apply to this book.

Pastor David and Pastor Chris, your book inspired me, just as your lives do, to become more and more like Jesus. Thank you for being such great role models to my husband, me, to the body of believers at GateWay City Church in San Jose, CA, and to the many people throughout the world you've influenced through your books and sermons. God bless you.

Daydreaming

Have you ever had a day in school where it seemed like the hands of the clock are frozen in time and going nowhere, just like you? Your eyes are on the teacher, but your mind is somewhere else, anywhere else rather than in a room filled with a ton of kids. Some are listening to the teacher's every word while other kids are like you, in their own little world.

Well, this is exactly what was happening to a student named Peter. As he drifted off, his memories brought him back to his home in Queens, New York. He could see everyone as if it were happening at that very moment. There were his Dad and his Mom and his big sister, Zoe, getting everything prepared for Christmas and for all of the houseguests, who were expected to arrive at any minute. Very soon, almost every square inch of their old three bedroom home would be filled with kids running from room to room while their parents shared their stories about "the good old days" with one another.

Next, his thoughts zoomed into what he considered the most cherished room in the house—his bedroom. He saw himself playing a video game that he bought with the money he earned cutting lawns during the summer. Awe, this was heaven—his very own hideaway where he could get lost in his own imaginary world and become the characters in his game, or surf the net for hours!

The bedrooms were off-limits to the houseguests, so he could find peace and quiet in his room. This made Peter smile as he reminisced. These memories brought Peter back to his very own "good old days," which he missed a lot. But now these memories would have to suffice because his parents were now missionaries and had answered the call to serve in the Amazon Rainforest.

At twelve years old, Peter had experienced his share of happiness, but his joy was eventually replaced with grief and sorrow for the many Indians that Peter and his family loved to serve in the remote areas of the Amazon. Many tribe members lost their lives to a common cold or the flu. Their immune systems weren't strong enough to battle these illnesses so they risked the chance of getting sick every time they came into town to trade for supplies. Peter and his family were always careful to visit the Indians when they were well and to stay at a safe distance when they visited the villages.

But illnesses weren't the only things that threatened the lives of these primitive people. Modern, industrious people who appreciated the financial value of the natural resources on the land that the tribes occupied, came in with large bulldozers and stripped the land of trees and coal. This forced the Indians to retreat even deeper into the rainforests to follow their food supply.

The harsh reality of their living conditions battled with Peter's mind and soon he started judging God by the challenges he saw in their lives. He didn't have the same joy, faith, and hope that his family had in the midst of all the pain and lack that surrounded them. He hadn't asked the Lord to come into his life. In fact, Peter cared for and knew more about the tribes than he knew about Jesus.

Peter lived in his own world of spiritual darkness. He stayed on the sidelines while his family and friends led people to Christ. Abraham Silva, who was named after Abraham in the Bible, was Peter's best friend. He was the adopted son of Peter's school teacher, Mr. Gabriel Silva. Abraham told Peter that he would rather have Jesus in his life than anything this world has to offer. This baffled Peter! How could Abraham make such a profound statement as that, after the life he came from?

Abraham was born in the slums of Rio de Janeiro, Brazil, and was found as a toddler wandering through South America's largest landfill. But God had an entirely different plan for his life and gave him a dad and a mom who were missionaries. They gave him a secure and loving home. Things were going great until the day Abraham came home from school to find that his mother had passed away.

Abraham's dad decided to take a job as a teacher at Peter's school. The father-and-son duo packed their belongings and set off for a new life and a new adventure. Mr. Silva and Abraham knew that they had a lot to share with others, so they asked the Lord for His help and inspiration. Peter couldn't understand why Abraham didn't aspire to have material things like he once had. If only Peter could turn back time.

Peter needed the ultimate Inspirer to bring contentment and love into his heart. He needed Jesus to live in his heart so he could live a life that inspired others. And until that happened Peter could not be used by God.

Gradually, Peter became bitter and his list of complaints started to grow and grow. Before he could get a grasp onto what was happening, he found himself pulling away from his family, barely talking with Abraham, and staying by himself more and more. He had no words to describe what he was feeling but one thing he knew for sure was that he was very sad. He was sad to see that what had started out as a pretty

5

normal life had become what it was now. But something was about to happen that would shake Peter's world and give him an entirely new perspective, one that would propel him to live an inspired life.

Shak'n Up

Peter was shocked back into reality as his teacher, Mr. Silva, began to yell out instructions to everyone in Portuguese.

Mr. Silva cried out, "We're having an earthquake! Everyone, run as fast as you can to the office where it's safe. Hurry! Don't waste any time!"

Peter instantly sprung up from the dirt-laden mat he'd been sitting on. There weren't any desks or chairs in this classroom nor were there computers or cell phones. The school was located in one of the most remote villages of the Amazon Rainforest. A typical day was spent in relative darkness as all of the thick vegetation that grew on the ground made its way up into the gnarled trees, blocking the rays of the sun from ever reaching the forest's damp, earthen floor below.

At Peter's school, all of the children from the village that he lived in gathered together in one big room to learn. From the oldest to the youngest they somehow managed to respect one another's space. Even without anything remotely close to what American kids are blessed to have in their classrooms, Peter and his classmates learned and excelled. His school was a two-story, run-down structure built on what was once a swamp. The constant heat and humidity left it almost impossible for the maintenance crew to keep a coat of paint from peeling off the walls. Most of the building remained unpainted, dirty, and dreary.

Peter ran as fast as he could towards the classroom doorway which led to the school office, but his classmates stampeded past him, around him, and eventually over him pushing him back into the thick, wet mud floor. Then with a sound like a train barreling down a track, the second floor above Peter began to pull away from its metal frame. The two cross beams that held the second floor together gave way, releasing all of the brick and stucco that made up the second floor walls onto Peter and the floor around him, pinning Peter's legs to the floor.

Abraham saved his father's life by pushing him away from an additional beam that narrowly missed hitting his dad in the head. The beam came down near where Peter was buried. Abraham bent down to help his dad up. They hugged each other tightly and knew that God had protected Gabriel from a fatal blow.

They quickly turned around to save Peter. They were running out of time and needed to act fast, so they both started frantically calling out Peter's name but Peter didn't respond. They wasted no time and began to dig through the heavy debris to get to Peter. Peter lay in the middle of two large heaps of rubble. He was going in and out of consciousness. It wasn't very long before he heard from far in the distance, his family's voices calling out his name and then, in what he thought was a blink, they were all standing near him.

"Oh Peter!" his mom cried. "Son? Is that you?" his dad asked. Peter's family was in shock as they stood there looking at him. Peter was almost unrecognizable and in desperate need of medical care. It took everything they had in them to keep from crying as they looked into his blackened eyes and surveyed all of his terrible injuries.

There was no time to waste so they quickly started organizing a plan to get him out of there. His mother, Maria, was a nurse and she could tell that Peter was starting to go into shock. He would die if they didn't get him to a hospital soon. But they had a major problem. They were hours away from any hospital and, with Peter's injuries being as bad as they were, there was no telling if he'd even arrive there alive. He had lost a lot of blood from the many gashes and open wounds that exposed his organs, bones, veins, and tissues throughout his body. And if that wasn't enough, when the beams came falling down they shattered both of his legs. Maria silently prayed to the Lord to help them get him to the hospital before it was too late.

They quickly put some boards together and wrapped them with curtains from the windows in the classroom, to create a stretcher to transport Peter out of what now looked like a war zone. And now, what they were all dreading was staring them right in the face. There was no way to avoid the inevitable. They knew that once they started to move Peter, the pain he was feeling would become unbearable, so they braced themselves for what was to come. They used the remaining curtains for tourniquets and then Peter's dad put his wallet in Peter's mouth and instructed him to chew down on it for the pain. Just as they expected, when they lifted Peter up high enough to get the boards underneath him, he screamed out in anguish, bit down on the wallet as hard as he could, then completely passed out from the pain.

Mr. Silva and Abraham helped Peter's family get him into their van. After they said their goodbyes, Abraham and his dad ran to the office to check on the other kids. His dad also needed to get on the Ham radio set and make an important call.

Just as they were about to start out on the long journey ahead of them, first by car, and then several hours by boat, Mr.

Silva ran up to the van yelling, "Stop! Stop! I have great news! I have friends who work on a medical rescue jet. At this very moment, they're setting everything up to transport Peter to the hospital and all of you can join him on board. The jet is fully equipped with a doctor, a nurse, and everything Peter needs to stabilize him until he goes into surgery."

Mr. Silva handed them a note showing them where the airport was. This was the answer to Maria's prayer! She thanked the Lord, and then she asked Mr. Silva if Abraham could join them. He said, "Yes!" and then he hugged his son goodbye. He knew in his heart that it was important for Abraham to be there with his friend and that God was going to use this terrible accident to reach Peter.

In the Flying Hospital

When they got to the airport, the doctor and nurse greeted them outside the streamlined jet with sanitized masks, gowns, and gloves to wear on the trip. They needed the cabin to remain as clean and sterile as possible, especially since Peter had open wounds. When Peter's family and Abraham stepped inside, they couldn't believe what they were seeing. It looked exactly like a hospital emergency room. The only difference was that this one could take the patient anywhere in the world in record time.

The doctor and nurse quickly hooked Peter up to all types of monitors and gave him medication for the pain. It wasn't long before he had an IV in one arm feeding him fluids so he wouldn't dehydrate, while another IV fed antibiotics into his body so he wouldn't get an infection. Soon, he was hooked up to a unit of blood through another IV to replenish the blood he had already lost. Peter was now prepared to go into surgery as soon as they arrived at the hospital.

Awash in the fresh smell of sanitizers and alcohol they all knew that this was the cleanest place they had been in for years! They surrounded Peter as he lay there totally dependent on the wonderful medical team that Mr. Silva had set up for Peter. Tears rolled down all of their faces as there was nothing they could do for him but pray! All they kept thinking was, "Peter still isn't saved!"

Zoe prayed out loud, "Please Jesus, spare my brother's life and show him what a loving and compassionate God you are! We know Peter is very stubborn, but you had a Peter on your team, too, and look what a great and solid disciple he became. So, we're entrusting our Peter to you, to guide and mold him carefully into the Man of God you will call him to be one day. Thank you, Jesus, for giving Peter your favor! In Your Holy Name, Jesus, we ask these things." Everyone joined in agreement with Zoe by saying, "Amen!"

Peter continued to drift in and out of consciousness. During one of these episodes where he blacked out, his mind strayed back to when his parents pastored a small multicultural church in Queens, New York. Peter was only seven years old and his sister, Zoe, was thirteen. They were good kids but, as with most PKs (Preacher's Kids), they were watched as though they lived in a fish bowl. Some of the congregation left them alone and let them be kids, while others expected them to be perfect. They felt that since they were representing their parents in public they had better shine in every way.

Zoe took it in stride, but it deeply affected Peter, especially after an elderly man in the church came up to Peter, called him a very mean name, and then declared that Peter "would amount to nothing when he grew up!" Peter couldn't shake it off or forget about it. He started to ask himself if it were true. Then he started to wonder if other people were thinking the same things about him. He was too scared to share it with anyone. Not with his parents, nor his sister. Not with his

Sunday school teacher, the rest of his family, his buddy Abraham, and certainly not with Jesus! Jesus was the last person on earth that he would ever want to share these terrible secrets with, but what he didn't realize was that Jesus knows **everything** about us, even our deepest, most painful secrets like the ones Peter was afraid to share with Him.

Peter also didn't know that Jesus was the one and only person who could fully understand exactly what he was feeling. Even though Jesus was born 100% God, perfect in every way, people still found fault with Him and called Him unkind names. Jesus was also 100% human, so He had the ability to choose to sin, but He never did. He didn't give in to the temptations from the enemy. He didn't retaliate when people were mean to Him. He lived a perfect, selfless life filled with love, compassion, forgiveness, grace, and mercy for all of mankind.

From Adam and Eve, Abraham and his sons, Isaac and Ishmael, to the millions of people of every color and every walk of life who were ever born, who are alive today, or will be born, Jesus gave His life on the cross and shed His blood for the forgiveness of all their sins. Everyone who asks Him to be their Lord and Savior will be heirs in His kingdom and live with Him forever.

Peter's family had given up preaching to him because they knew that only Jesus could get through to Peter. He was set in his ways, so they all continued to pray that the day would come when Jesus would speak into Peter's heart. Even Abraham knew that if he wanted to remain as Peter's friend, he had to stop talking to him about the Lord and so he did.

In a short time, the jet landed. An ambulance and car met them at the airport. They were now only minutes away from the hospital. Just as the ambulance doors opened, Peter began to have seizures as his temperature peaked to a dangerous high. There was no time to lose. Peter's family kissed him goodbye as he was whisked away to be prepared for reconstructive surgery on his legs and to repair all of the other injuries he had all over his body. The doctor promised that it was going to be a very long night and he kept his promise.

The Visitor

Many hours later, when Peter was in his hospital room, he was awakened out of sleep by an entirely new pain, one he had never experienced before in his life. This pain gripped his brain and it was impossible for him to even lift his head off of the pillow. Excruciating pain sent him frantically searching for the call button. Maria, who was in the room, saw it all happening and called for the nurse. Peter blacked out.

Peter's room quickly filled with nurses and doctors working frantically over him to help him regain consciousness. He could hear them talking and asking him question; but he couldn't respond to them, couldn't open his eyes, couldn't move the rest of his body. Somehow, as odd as it might sound, Peter felt safe as he began to believe that his life was coming to an end and he'd no longer be feeling any more pain.

After a battery of tests, he heard the doctor in the room tell his parents, Mark and Maria, that he was in a coma and that

19

the doctors would be monitoring his brain waves for the next few days. They would take an MRI to see to what extent Peter's head had been injured during the accident. Then he heard his parents begin to sob and pray over him.

At that point, Peter wanted so badly to yell, "No! Really, I'm fine! Don't worry Mom and Dad! I just checked out because of the pain that I felt, but really I'm still here!" But he couldn't! Feeling helpless, confused, and worst of all, hopeless, Peter gave into what he could no longer control: his destiny. This was exactly what Someone needed to have happen so He could sit down and speak with Peter without any distractions. And that Someone was Jesus.

Jesus pulled up a chair beside Peter's bed and, with kindness and compassion, He took Peter's hands and gently laid them between His nail pierced hands. Peter felt His hands and knew in an instant Who was in the room with him.

As Peter lay there, with Jesus holding his hands, all of the things about Jesus that Peter's parents had told him over the years flooded his heart. He was immersed in love! All of the worship music he'd ever heard filled the room. Peter listened to a choir of angels singing as they stood around the room, praising and worshiping God with the most beautiful voices he had ever heard. Peter also saw several cherubs flying above them with so much grace and ease that it was as though they were giving glory to the Lord as they flew.

He knew he was in the presence of the living God, the One who takes away the sins of the world. But Peter had some business that he needed to talk over with Jesus, man to man. He knew that Jesus could not lie and that He would answer his questions honestly. So he began asking Jesus those questions as respectfully and carefully as he could since he wasn't sure if he'd ever have this chance again. Jesus was touched by Peter's reverence for Him and planned to stay with Peter for however long it took for Peter to understand Him. Peter started off the conversation by asking Jesus, "Could you please tell me, Jesus, if You're here with me because I'm about to die?"

Jesus answered, "No Peter, you're not about to physically die."

Peter replied, "Okay, that's a relief! Then, why are you here Jesus?"

Jesus said, "I'm here because I need to answer the questions that make you have doubts about Me. You're growing further and further away from Me and, one day, you'll have such a hardened heart towards the things of God that it'll be impossible to have a conversation as we're having together right now. Please Peter, ask me what you've been wanting to ask me. You know that I'll give you an honest answer."

Peter said, "Okay, I will. Here are my questions. Why did you put the tree that brought death into the Garden of Eden if you loved Adam and Eve?"

Jesus relied, "Adam and Eve were created each with their own free will. They were not created to be like robots or to be like slaves who obey everything they are told to do by their Master. When you love someone you want them to freely

22

love you back, not because they have to, but because they want to. That's what true love is all about."

Peter replied, "Wow, I never thought about it that way, but that makes total sense. Okay, here's another question that I have. You see evil in all the world yet You do nothing to end it. Why not?"

Jesus replied, "Once again, Peter, it goes back to humans being created with their own free will. Adam and Eve allowed sin in the world by the choices that they made. If evil were abolished right now, your free will would also be taken away, because you would be living a perfect life without having to make a choice between good and evil."

"I see your point, Jesus." Peter said, "Now for my last and final question. If you knew before the foundation of the earth was made that your creation, man and woman, would turn against you, why did you make them anyway?"

Jesus replied, "Because I wanted to have a relationship with them, and with all of you, because I love you!"

With that last answer, Peter heard, and most importantly felt in his soul, the deep love and compassion that Jesus had for His creation. Peter realized that as much as Jesus would love to have everyone that He'd ever created love Him, He knew that it wouldn't be genuine love without the choice. That's why He gave everyone a free will. People could make their own choices to love things that edify God or love things that edify the evil one.

Jesus began to tell Peter His story of love and redemption for His creation. He said, "From Adam and Eve to the days of Noah and the world wide-flood, from Sodom and Gomorrah to idol worshipers, Satan has been busy at work deceiving God's creation by diverting their attention away from the things of God and toward things that bring sinful pleasures. It wasn't very long before people's hearts became hardened against the commandments of God, and soon more and more perversion entered the world.

"Everyone was in desperate need of a Savior! A Savior who could forgive them of their sins and offer them eternal life in exchange for their transgressions. God the Father loved them way too much to give up on them, so He had His son, me, take on flesh and come down to earth as a baby. I was born by the power of the Holy Spirit to a young woman named Mary. That was the day I was given the name 'Jesus,' which means, in Hebrew, 'God Saves.' I was born in the town of Bethlehem, the same town where the perfect, unblemished, sacrificial lambs were born and raised to be burned on the altars for the atonement of Israel's sins.

"I'm 100% God and 100% Man, something no person on earth could, or ever will be able to truthfully say they are. I've never sinned. I hate sin, but I love the sinner and after I've forgiven a sin, I can't remember the sin forever more. This is my nature.

"Growing up, my life was filled with adventure! From having to flee with my parents to Egypt because King Herod was trying to have me killed, to returning to the town of Nazareth and working alongside my earthly father, Joseph, as a carpenter, my life has never been boring. As a young boy around your age, Peter, I began to study God's word and eventually I became a Semikhah Rabbi. I had the honor of having the first choice to take the brightest students in the seminary under my mentorship, but I chose to mentor ordinary men instead.

"Just before I went into ministry, I was baptized by my cousin, John the Baptist, in the Jordan River. There, my Father in Heaven sent the Holy Spirit in the form of a dove to me and He said from heaven, 'This is my beloved Son, in whom I am well pleased.' I was now ready to take on one of the biggest tests of my life as I went into the wilderness, without any food, to pray. I was tempted by Satan for forty days and nights, but through the power of the Holy Spirit, my flesh didn't give into my earthly cravings to eat and I passed the exam with flying colors!

"At thirty years old, I began my ministry which lasted three and a half years, and during this wonderful period of time, my twelve disciples went with me from village to village, teaching everyone, young and old, the gospel. I performed many miracles: resurrected people from the dead, fed the poor, and healed people of every color and creed. We shared with them the message of forgiveness, love, and eternal salvation.

"My goal, during those three and a half years, was to show people, through the example of my own life, what an Inspirer looked and acted like and how they could inspire others to do the same. Living the Inspired Life should be something everyone desires to do and they should want everyone else to live inspired as well!

"During those years of my ministry on earth, I never lost my focus on the prize that was set before me—to win souls. No matter how hard my life had become and how increasingly mean the Priests at the temple and synagogues were to me, I humbly held my head up and remembered why I was sent. I never retaliated after all of the harsh treatment I received.

"It was during this time that one of my very own disciples, Judas of Iscariot, betrayed me by disclosing my whereabouts to the chief priests and elders for thirty pieces of silver. Judas identified me to them by kissing me on my cheek. Some might say it was the kiss of death, but I knew how the story would end so I went willingly. I forgave Judas, but he couldn't forgive himself, so his life that night came tragically to an end.

"The day finally arrived when all my enemies wanted me silenced as I continued to declare that I was the Son of God. I had proved it over and over by the lives that were changed forever. I was beaten and then whipped with strong strands of leather embossed with flesh tearing metal and bones. They encircled my head with a crown they made from long, sharp thorns and pushed it down into my forehead and scalp. Then they laid me on a cross and nailed my hands and feet to the wood. They raised the cross up and planted it in the dirt. There I died next to a murderer and a thief and over my head they mockingly posted a sign that read, 'Jesus, King of the Jews.'

"In Mark 15:25-39, the author describes how I hung on the cross from 9 a.m. to 3 p.m. Those were the exact same hours of each day that the Jews in the Temple practiced their daily sacrifice. They sacrificed two perfect, unblemished male lambs and prayed for a redeemer, the forgiveness of sins, the coming of the Messiah, and the resurrection of the dead.

"I was the answer then, and I am still the answer today, and forever, to all who cry out for me to be their Lord and Savior. I became the perfect, unblemished Lamb of God who takes away the sins of the world. Even though I didn't deserve to die, I went without a fight. I took my last breath and uttered my final words, 'Father, into your hands I commit my spirit.' Death had no hold on me and three days later I walked out of the tomb in which my body had been laid. It is through me and only me that people who accept me as their Lord and Savior can live with me eternally in Heaven.

Miracles Abound!

Jesus knew that Peter was still holding on to a very deep hurt in his life that was preventing him from moving forward, so Jesus said, "All through your lifetime here on earth, Peter, you will find that there are people who, for whatever reason, are joy robbers. They'll call you names or say mean things to you that just aren't true just to make themselves feel better about their own miserable lives. Many times they have acted from jealousy or they were put into your life by the enemy to discourage you. But Peter, do what I always told my disciples: forgive them and bless them and your heavenly Father who sees your suffering will bless you because you did what was right."

Peter smiled as he listened to Jesus' wise counsel. He was amazed that Jesus knew exactly what was hurting him and how to take care of the problem. Peter had a decision to make.

He knew deep down in his heart that this was the moment when his life would never be the same again!

Peter smiled at Jesus, rose up out of his bed, and stood up onto his feet without even thinking about the impossibility of what he had just done. He hugged Jesus tightly and then he began to weep. While wrapped in Jesus' arms, he let go of all of the disappointments in his life, the hurts of the past, and the shame that he carried for the way he tried to shut out his family, his buddy Abraham, and most importantly, Jesus.

Jesus knew that Peter had come to the end of himself— looking out for what made him happy all the time instead of what he could do to bring glory and honor to God. Peter began to talk through all the tears and with every word, the hole in his heart got smaller and smaller.

"Jesus," Peter wept, "I need You to be the Lord of my life starting right now. I've been so selfish and I've lost a lot of time thinking only about myself. I'm asking for Your forgiveness and for You to make me into Your servant. I want to inspire others to become just like You, Lord. I promise to keep You involved in everything that I plan to do. I ask You for Your guidance and Your wisdom so I don't continue to walk through life alone and without Your plan. I love you, Jesus! Please Jesus, come and live in my heart today!" Instantly, Peter knew he was changed as God's love filled his heart to overflowing. He could feel the joy and peace he had been missing.

Then Jesus said his parting words to Peter, "You, Peter, are forgiven and are now my son. You have a commission here on earth to reach the lost, but I don't want you to do this alone. I want you to surround yourself with believers who have been inspiring others for a long time, such as your family, Mr. Silva, and Abraham. Trust me, they all know what it means to love me and to love my children even when they've gone through tremendous losses in their own lives. They all have life changing testimonies that will inspire you to become more and more like me. I'm the person they have modeled their lives after, which brings me so much honor and blessing!

"And Peter, there's one last thing that you'll need to share with your doctor. Ask him to take the casts off of your legs because they're completely healed. And he'll need to look at all of the wounds that you had. Yes, you are completely healed!"

Instantly, Peter realized at that moment that he had been standing that whole time on two healed legs while conversing with his Savior, and he didn't even know it! As Peter began to cry once again, Jesus gave him a big hug and helped him to get back in bed before He left Peter's side.

"Remember, son," said Jesus, "I'm only a prayer away and my Holy Spirit is always with you. I love you, Peter!" Then, in a blink, Jesus was gone.

An Unexpected Blessing

Neither Peter's family, nor Abraham, had ever left Peter's side for three days. They prayed and fasted for him around the clock. They knew that it was only a matter of time before Jesus would reward their faith, so when they saw Peter start to move and his eye lids open up one by one, they began to thank Jesus for this wonderful miracle!

Mark shouted out, "Praise you, Jesus!" And soon, Zoe joined in by saying, "Thank you, Lord for healing Peter!"

Peter began to cry as he saw how much they loved him. Maria asked Peter, "Son, how are you feeling? Did you know that you've been in a coma for three days?"

Peter responded, "I'm feeling great, Mom. I knew I was in a coma, but I couldn't respond to you all those days. I felt so bad that I couldn't tell you that I was okay."

"We're so happy that we know who Jesus is, because we called out for Him to heal you, Peter." said Abraham.

"And that's exactly what He did!" exclaimed Peter.

Peter told them, "But He did more than that, everyone, He saved my soul! I had an encounter with Jesus while I was gone those three days and I gave Him my life!" Tears rolled down everyone's faces as they wrapped their arms around each other and lifted their heads praising and thanking Jesus.

Just then, the doctor walked past Peter's room, then quickly walked back for a second look. Was he seeing things? This couldn't be! Peter was sitting up in bed, talking and laughing. The doctor hurried into the room to see what was happening, and instantly he was drawn into the presence of God. He knew Jesus' presence from his childhood, but he had strayed away in his adult years. He had lost interest in the Lord when God didn't heal his patients the way he wanted them to be healed. The doctor didn't want to allow God to be God and make His own sovereign decisions, so gradually he squeezed Jesus out of his life.

But the Spirit of God touched him in Peter's room and within seconds, tears began to roll down his face. He laid face down on the floor worshiping Jesus and asking His forgiveness for trying to use God instead of trusting in Him. He knew that Peter being awake was a miracle, but Peter had even more miracles to show him.

Peter called him over to the bed and said, "Doctor, I've been with Jesus for the past three days and Jesus told me to tell you that He wants you to take the casts off of my legs and to look at my wounds." The doctor reached into his pocket for his scissors and then he carefully cut back the hard casts. To his amazement, both of Peter's legs, which had been shattered by the accident and held together by pins and rods, were in perfect condition, healed and whole, with no scars whatsoever! And that wasn't all. The rest of Peter's body was perfect and there were no scars or bruises anywhere to be found.

The doctor composed himself the best way he knew how, and began to tell them about a young girl who years ago had been brought into the hospital after she had been hit by a bus. He said, "Her legs were shattered just like Peter's legs were. I did all that I could to save her legs. I reconstructed them, prayed for her, and believed that God would allow her to one day walk again. But God had a different plan that I was in total disagreement with. She eventually had to have both legs amputated.

Somehow, I had it in my mind that if my faith was big enough I could expect Jesus to do whatever I asked him to do for me. But what I was actually doing was trying to control God. When I realized that I couldn't, I walked away from Him; as a result, I have had this emptiness in my life ever since. This is a miracle not only for you, Peter, but also is exactly what Jesus wanted me to see so I would regain my faith in Him. Yes, Jesus is still into creating miracles and, Peter, we all have a lot to thank Him for!"

Peter Finds Out

On the way home the next day, Mark handed Peter a newspaper as he got into the back seat of their rented van. It would relate to Peter all of the things that happened the day he was admitted into the hospital. There it was in big, bold print, **"Major Earthquake Rips through the Amazon Rainforest."**

Peter felt chills go up his spine as he stared at the graphic pictures showing what was left of his school—literally, nothing! He couldn't believe his eyes! The school was flattened! And alongside the picture of devastation was a story about his teacher, Mr. Silva, and his son Abraham, Peter's friend, who were being hailed by all of the school's students as "Courageous Heroes."

Peter read, "Not only had they helped almost all of the students to escape from the classroom to the safety of the school office, which suffered only minor damage, but they also dug out to safety, Peter Vasquez, who was trapped under a huge pile of rubble. Two heavy beams from the floor above came down and crushed both of Peter's legs, pinning him to the floor. Then stucco and brick hit Peter in the head, leaving him non responsive."

The next page showed a picture of Peter being carried on the stretcher into a private jet with his parents, sister, and rescuer, Abraham, by his side. The article also stated that when Peter arrived at the hospital the doctor had said that "he would do all that he could to save Peter's legs."

When Peter read in the article that Mr. Silva had asked the people who lived in their village, as well as people in neighboring villages, to pray for Peter, and that they had been holding nightly prayer vigils for him, he cried. He knew that God had answered all of their prayers.

Other people in the region weren't as blessed as Peter and his classmates. It had been a ruthless quake that claimed many victims in its vicinity. Peter looked at his family with such a thankful heart! They, too, could've been among the many others who lost their lives that day. They had a lot to thank Jesus for.

Just as he was about to tell them how blessed they all were, God put it into his heart to do something very important, something his former self would never have done in a million years! Peter cried out, "Mom, Dad, we need to turn this van around and head back to the hospital, quick!"

Maria called out in fear, "Are you alright son? Are you feeling sick?"

Peter replied, "Everything's fine. Trust me. I believe that Jesus just told me how we can help all of the people who lost loved ones and everything in the earthquake. It's going to be as simple as setting up a news conference with my doctor, and with the same newspaper reporter who did this story on the earthquake and on all of us."

Peter remembered what Jesus had told him about everyone having their own testimonies, so he decided to encourage his family and friend to share their stories, too, at this very important event. Peter then filled them in on all the details and he asked Abraham to help him set it all up.

The journey back to the hospital was short so they had to plan what they were going to say, and do, very quickly. Peter knew that all of their stories needed to be told so God would be glorified and people would be helped through their testimonies.

Amazing Stories

As they pulled into the circular driveway of the hospital they saw several reporters walking to their cars. The place was swarming with news vans, but everyone looked sad and disappointed. Mark got out to ask a reporter what was happening.

"Awe," said one reporter, "We were hoping to interview a kid named Peter Vasquez, but it looks like we just missed him. Everyone is talking about him. Seems he had a great miracle happen to him. You know, it's not every day that something like that happens and, as a Christian, I wanted other people to see what a great God I serve!"

Pastor Mark responded to him by announcing, "Well, you won't have to wait any longer for your interview, because our son, Peter, is here to answer all of your questions."

Peter jumped out of the van and the reporters who were there motioned for their camera men to join them. They kept looking at his legs. They stared at him wonderingly as though he were the prototype of a brand new toy. They were in awe!

Maria ran into the hospital to get the doctor and, within minutes, they were set to have a news conference the likes of which the hospital had never seen before. The doctor brought out pictures of what Peter's legs looked like when he first came into the hospital, as well as pictures of all the open wounds he had all over his body. And now, astonishingly, they were looking at Peter's new and improved legs and perfect body after Jesus had healed him.

As reporters gathered around him and held out their microphones, Peter began his speech. "Thank you all for coming here and allowing me, my family, and my best friend Abraham, to share with you our message of life and hope. I would not be here today had it not been for their faith in Jesus and for all the countless people who joined in and prayed for me. Because of their prayers, I'm healed.

"Up until yesterday, I was walking in spiritual darkness and I didn't want to have a relationship with God. But many people had been praying for my soul. Today, I stand before you forgiven and a follower of Jesus.

"As you can see from the newspaper, and my doctor's pictures, it's no wonder why I went into a coma. It is a wonder that I'm able to speak to you today while standing on two perfectly strong legs that just four days ago were shattered!"

The reporters cheered as Peter spoke, and took lots of pictures as if Peter were a celebrity on the red carpet. Peter loved every minute of the attention because this wasn't his moment, this was all about Jesus. This was about what Jesus could do for them, and what they could do for the people who experienced great losses in the earthquake.

Peter continued to speak. "I pray that as we share our testimonies with you today, that you will realize that you, too, need to have Jesus in your lives. And now, I'd like to introduce you to my closest friend, who's more like a brother to me, Abraham Silva."

Abraham spoke, "Thank you everyone for your applause, but the Man of the hour, to whom we owe all honor for this great and wonderful miracle, is Jesus Christ. Jesus is the same yesterday, today, and forever. He's not finished creating miracles yet, and believe you me, I'm one of them.

"I was born thirteen years ago and came from a life of poverty, living in the Jardim Gramacho Landfill, a garbage dump which was the size of around 200 football fields. I dug through rat infested piles of rotted food to get my daily meal. I was abandoned by my mother who, God rest her soul, was then a young teen with no hope and no future. She vanished off the face of the earth one day.

"But God was watching over me and gave me a wonderful father and mother, by the names of Gabriel and Esther Silva, who adopted me and introduced me to Jesus

Christ. My life changed the day I asked Jesus to come into my heart, and I've been so blessed ever since!

"Later, my mom passed away and my father took a job as the teacher at mine and Peter's school in the Amazon."

After hearing Abraham's testimony, Peter realized that he had more in common with Abraham than ever before. They both had miraculous testimonies of how God had saved their lives—and souls—from eternal destruction. It was now their turn to show the Lord just how grateful they each were to Him for such wonderful gifts.

After the applause died down, you could hear a pin drop as everyone waited to hear what Peter and the rest of his family had to share.

Peter said, "Thank you, Abraham, for sharing your testimony with us. Now I would like to introduce you to my awesome parents, Pastor Mark Vasquez and Pastor Maria Vasquez."

Pastor Mark took his place in front of the microphones and tried to hold back the tears as he shared his story of redemption with the large crowd that was growing by the minute. He started, "When I was a young teen, I got involved in a street gang in New York. I did things that I'm too ashamed to talk about, although I was held accountable for them.

"While I was serving time, a Chaplain came into one of our group meetings and shared with us the true life story about a man named Jesus who wanted to forgive us, and pardon us, of our sins. Hardened gang members began to weep that day as they heard about all of the things Christ did for them when He was nailed to the cross. I was so moved by the dramatic changes that I witnessed in the lives of these men that later, while alone in my cell, I asked Jesus to be the Lord of my life. I also asked the Chaplain to bring me a Bible the next time he met with us.

"After I was released from jail back into the home of my family, who didn't care about what happened to me, I wasn't alone. I now had Jesus and instead of carrying a weapon on me, I carried my Bible wherever I went. That's how I finally met my beautiful wife, Maria." Pastor Mark then had Maria step in front of the microphones.

Maria began to give her testimony. "My story is boring in comparison, but it proves how Jesus can use someone to inspire others to look beyond what they've been given in life.

"I was born into a very rich, affluent family of doctors who didn't have the need for God. I attended all of the best schools throughout my childhood, and college was no exception. I was attending a prestigious medical school and preparing to take my exams to be licensed as a registered nurse in the state of New York. I had worked very hard for many years towards this goal and I wasn't about to let anything or anyone get me off track.

"But one day, I took a different path back to the dorms and bumped into a young street preacher. Long story short, I graduated, became a registered nurse, and got my title as Mrs.

Vasquez only fourteen months before our first baby, Zoe, was born.

"And within a year, I co-pastored with my husband at a wonderful multi-cultural church in Queens, New York. My life is nothing like I ever imagined it would be. But I thank God, because I was empty without Jesus in my life. So, let me introduce to you our beautiful daughter, Zoe."

"Thanks, Mom!" Zoe said as she stepped up to the microphones. "Yes, my name is Zoe," she continued, "which some of you may not know means eternal life. I'm a missionary in the Amazon Rainforest and I'm very blessed to serve the Lord alongside my two great parents who have brought honor and praise to God by the way they live their lives for Jesus.

"It was through their example that I gave my life to Jesus. All of our family on both sides, also have given their lives over to Jesus. My parents didn't need to preach: their lives did the speaking for them.

"I'm eighteen years old now and I know that when the time is right, Jesus will bring me a Godly husband that He's hand-chosen especially for me. Until then, I put my trust in Jesus because He's never let me down and He can do the same for you. And now, we come full circle as my baby brother, Peter, would like to speak with you again."

People Respond

"Hi everyone," Peter began, "you've heard all of our testimonies today. Our God, Jesus Christ, is real and He wants to have a lasting relationship with each and every one of you today!

"Four days ago, just after I went into a coma, Jesus pulled up a seat next to my hospital bed. We spoke and He never left my side for those three days. During this time, while I was being healed by Jesus, the doctor and his team were working frantically over my body to help me regain consciousness. And everyone was praying and crying over my vegetative frame.

"None of this rattled Jesus. Here I was in the eye of the storm and Jesus calmly led me out of it. He miraculously healed my shattered legs, He took away all of my scars, and He healed my injured brain. And He instantly took away all of the excruciating pain that I was experiencing after the accident.

"I realized in the very short time that I was with Jesus, that I had never before taken the time to get to know Him. I had never learned how valuable each and every one of us are to Him. I finally realized that He's a gentleman who lives in our hearts only if we invite Him in.

"We're going to give you an opportunity to do just that in a moment. We'll pray the 'sinner's prayer' and each of you can receive Jesus into your heart today. Dad, could you please lead everyone in this very special prayer?"

Pastor Mark came forward and said, "I'd be honored to, son." He faced the crowd and said, "Would you please bow your heads and, if you'd like to ask Jesus to live in your heart, please repeat this prayer after me. 'Lord, I come to You as a sinner, needing to be forgiven of all my sins. Please forgive me, Jesus. I know that You're the Son of God, and I'm inviting You, right now, to come and live inside my heart. Jesus, please help me every day to become more and more like You. I ask these things in Your precious name. Thank you, Jesus! Amen!"

When Pastor Mark looked around at the crowd of people, he could see that many had given their lives to Christ. Some were gathered around other believers crying with joy, while others beamed with God's peace stamped across their faces. It was a wonderful time with eternal rewards for everyone there who had made Jesus the Lord of his or her life!

For the last time, Peter stood in front of the mics and shared with everyone what was heavy on his heart: the needs of everyone else who didn't have a happy ending to their story when, four days ago, the earthquake took down their homes, businesses, factories, schools, and bridges.

He said, "If I could please have your attention one last time. Thank you. I stand before you asking not for myself, but for the Lord that I serve, Jesus Christ, that you will all help us to feed, clothe, and give new shelter to those who lost their loved ones and homes in this horrific earthquake. We are welcoming you all to join us as we begin our long journey into the remote villages and towns where the devastation was the greatest. Thank you, and God bless you all!"

Just as they were about to leave, doctors and nurses surrounded Peter's van with first aid supplies. People from the crowd came up to them and gave them money to buy whatever they needed for the people they were about to bless. Peter, Abraham, and Peter's family then got into their van to go home. All of the reporters then ran to their vans, cars, and trucks and formed a caravan into the dark regions of the Amazon Rainforest.

Soon reports and pictures were circulated throughout the region, then spread throughout the world, about the needs of these poor people who went from barely surviving to having nothing at all. Humanitarian aid came and soon schools were rebuilt, bridges were reconstructed, and the survivors were connected with people who truly loved and cared for them.

As the regions became refortified, more souls were saved by Jesus. People were inspired to do more for others as they became inspired themselves. You see, the miracle that happened to Peter and the testimonies of all his family, and his friend Abraham, inspired everyone from far and near to be an inspiration to others.

People found that they had a purpose in life. They didn't need to hike to the highest peak to find peace, for the Prince of Peace now resided in their hearts and gave them His perfect peace.

What can you do to become an Inspirer, you ask? Do what Pastor Mark and Pastor Maria did. They started their inspired life journey by first dedicating their hearts and lives to Jesus. Then they made commitments to the Lord to always pray to Him and ask Him for direction in every area of their lives.

They read their Bibles daily because it not only fed their souls, but taught them how to live a life that brings honor and glory to God. And when they were confident that they were firmly planted in the foundation of God's teachings, they began to reach out to others and teach them about Jesus.

Through these daily habits, they became more and more like Jesus every day. They fed, clothed, and housed the poor. And just like the Lord, they prayed over sick and dying people, and received many miracles.

Remember this very important point. You don't have to be a pastor or a missionary to be used by God to bless others. You can be a kid, a teen, an adult in college, a mother at home with children, or a man working twelve hour days to be used by the Lord to inspire others.

So let your light shine before everyone, and soon people will be drawn to the One who lives inside of you, Jesus. And they, too, will be inspired to live the inspired life where everyone lives to please God and bring more people into the Lord's kingdom.

Kathy King's Biography

In Matthew 12:33-37 (New King James Version), Jesus clearly tells us what He feels about the use of words:

> "Either make the tree good and its fruit good, or else make the tree bad and its fruit bad; for a tree is known by its fruit. Brood of vipers! How can you, being evil, speak good things? For out of the abundance of the heart the mouth speaks. A good man out of the good treasure of his heart brings forth good things, and an evil man out of the evil treasure brings forth evil things. But I say to you that for every idle word men may speak, they will give account of it in the Day of Judgment. For by your words you will be justified, and by your words you will be condemned."

Kathy King takes these words of Jesus very seriously. After a close self-examination of her heart, she can confidently state that her motives behind writing this book were completely born out of the love that she has for God, and for children. It's her heart's desire that children everywhere realize that their lives are empty if they don't have a personal relationship with Jesus.

Jesus is the greatest life coach a kid could ever have. Jesus lived through the unimaginable without sinning, died for our sins, and resurrected from the dead so that whoever asks Him to live in their heart will live with Him for eternity.

It's also Kathy's desire for this book to ignite a passion into the hearts of every child to pray for their family, friends, neighbors, and people throughout the world who need Jesus in their lives, so they, too, can live a life inspired by God.

Kathy is a wife, mother, and grandmother, and attends GateWay City Church in San Jose, California, with her husband, Jeff. She's a graduate of IMPACT! School of Ministry and Timothy Force. She's also a graduate of the Cleansing Stream Discipleship Program. She served in Cleansing Stream Ministry for several years and has been the Children's Director for Newborns to Preschoolers at her church for nearly ten years. She's also an elder and a licensed minister.

Contact Kathy King at: kathyk@gccsj.com

Made in the USA
San Bernardino, CA
09 February 2016